STAR WARS® ADVENTURES

Trouble on Tatooine
GAME BOOK

STAR WARS

ADVENTURES
GAME BOOK

Trouble on Tatooine

Dave Wolverton

LUCAS BOOKS

SCHOLASTIC INC.

New York • Toronto • London • Auckland • Sydney
Mexico City • New Delhi • Hong Kong • Buenos Aires

ISBN 0-439-45899-4

12 11 10 9 8 7 6 5 4 3 2   3 4 5 6 7 8/0

Printed in the U.S.A.

First Scholastic printing, April 2000

Trouble on Tatooine

YOUR ADVENTURE BEGINS

For the full story behind your adventure, read up to page 33 in your *Star Wars* Adventures novel, *Trouble on Tatooine*. Or begin here.

You are Anakin, Pala, Dorn, Kitster, or Arawynne. The *Adventure Guide* includes the rules for your *Star Wars* Adventure. You must follow these rules at all times.

Gardulla the Hutt has captured Pala, Dorn, Kitster, and the Ghostling children. On Tatooine one thing is very clear: Slaves who try to escape face the ultimate punishment. Gardulla has taken the children to the arena at Mos Espa to await public execution.

Anakin has crawled up into the cell through the Mos Espa drainage system with only a few tools.

Your job is to lead the children through the sand drains as they try to escape. It's a dirty job, but someone has to do it.

Choose your character. Each character has unique talents that are listed on his or her character card. You can only use Power three times on this adventure.

You start this adventure with your Adventure Point (AP) total from your previous adventure, or 1000 AP, if this is your first adventure.

May the Force be with you!

YOUR ADVENTURE:

TROUBLE ON TATOOINE

You've entered the drainage system and have found your friends. Above you, guards are shouting, "Sound the alarm!"

Sand is everywhere. It blows in your hair, mouth, and clothes. Each of you needs a sandmask, just to make it through the pipes. You don't want anyone to choke.

You're last in line, following the other children through the narrow pipe. You have to squeeze to get through, pushing with your toes, and wriggling your shoulders. It's hard work.

You concentrate on breathing through your mouth, inhaling through your sand-mask.

The group only has three glow rods. Up front, the leader carries one. A child in the midst of the group takes another, and you hold the last. All that you can see are jumbled shadows and the feet and legs of the Ghostling boy that crawls directly ahead of you.

The pipes are hardly big enough for a child to squeeze through. You have to wriggle along through the sand, pulling yourself on your elbows, pushing with your toes.

You push the Jawa ion blaster ahead of you, along with a tool sack.

"I'm at a junction," one of your friends yells from ahead. "Which way do I go?"

Choose to find the right direction either with or without using Power.

To find the right direction (using Power)*: Choose your Compass Power or your Find Power. Roll the 20-dice. Your roll# + your navigation# + your Power# + your Power's low-resist# is your adventure#.

If your adventure# is equal to or more than 14, add the difference + 5 to your AP total. You know the area well. You remove your sandmask and shout, "Head down to the right! Go till the second pipe opens overhead. That will take us to the Podracer hangar." You may proceed.

If your adventure# is less than 14, subtract the difference from your AP total. You make a wrong turn and must try to find the right direction again. Go back "To find the right direction (using Power)," and repeat until you've found the right way.

*NOTE: This counts as one of three Power uses you are allowed on this adventure.

To find the right direction (without using Power): Roll the 20-dice. If navigation is one of your talents, your roll# + your knowledge# + your navigation# + 2 is your adventure#. If navigation is one not of your talents, your roll# + your knowledge# + your navigation# is your adventure#.

If your adventure# is equal to or more than 14, add the difference + 5 to your AP total. You know the arena well. You remove your sandmask and shout, "Head down and to the right! Go till the second pipe opens overhead. That will take us to the Podracer hangar." You may proceed.

If your adventure# is less than 14, subtract the difference from your AP total. You make a wrong turn and must try to find the right direction again. Go back "To find the right direction (without using Power)," and repeat until you've found the right way.

In the distance, you hear wailing alarms. They echo spookily through the pipes. You silently hope that the signal-jammers keep working. If they don't, someone's transmitter might give your location away.

"Watch out behind you," one of your friends shouts to you. "They'll be sending capture droids."

You knew that. The slave masters will probably send capture droids through the pipes, since they can work well in tight spaces.

Capture droids are made to hunt for fugitives. Like seekers, they track by scent. Their infrared eyes see in the dark. Their stunners can knock down even the biggest man. And once they get their claws into you, they won't let go.

Right now, you can't do anything to stop them. As long as you are stuck in this narrow pipe, you can't turn around to shoot your ion blaster.

You pull down your sandmask again. "Hurry!" you shout. You shove the sand-mask back over your face.

The children scurry as fast as they can. Overhead, behind you, you hear guards yelling, followed by the sound of a metal grate scraping against the pipes. As you crawl, you listen for the telltale sound of mechanical legs scrabbling at your back.

The little Ghostling boy in front of you suddenly stops, knee deep in some sand. He is at a juncture.

Behind you, you hear a scraping sound, the *rap, tap, tap* of mechanical feet scurrying through the pipes.

Three small pipes meet here in a box, then the sand drains into a wider pipe down below.

You dive headfirst into the sand at the junction and come up with your Jawa ion blaster. You don't dare stick your head up where the capture droid could get you.

You simply poke the ion blaster into the open pipe. It won't damage any living creatures, only droids.

To blast the capture droids: Choose your weapon. Roll the 10-dice. Your roll# + your weaponry# + your weapon's mid-range# + 1 is your adventure#.

If your adventure# is equal to or more than 9, add the difference + 10 to your AP total. With blasting like that, you ought to get a job as a droid disabler. You may proceed.

If your adventure# is less than 9, subtract the difference from your AP total. You hear more scrabbling in the pipes! Go back "To blast the capture droids," and repeat until you've taken care of the droids.

The blue ionized gases from your blaster roar through the pipe.

Three electronic vocoders squeal, echoing loudly in the enclosed space. Your mouth drops in astonishment. There were *three* capture droids in that pipe!

You glimpse a flash of light in the tunnel as one of the droids emits a shower of sparks. Proceed to dodge them either with or without using Power.

To dodge the sparks (using Power)*: Choose your Reflex Power or your Motion Power. Roll the 20-dice to escape the sparks. Your roll# + your stealth# + your Power# + your Power's mid-resist# is your adventure#.

If your adventure# is equal to or more than 14, add the difference + 15 to your AP total. You're so good at dodging sparks that you should join the Galactic Circus! You jump into the safety of the sand, and may proceed.

If your adventure# is less than 14 but more than or equal to 9, subtract the difference from your AP total. The exploding sparks nearly ignite your head. Hopefully, the burnt-hair look will be in this year. The force of the blast knocks you into the sand. You may proceed.

If your adventure# is less than 9, subtract 30 from your AP total. Ouch! You're burnt pretty seriously. It's going to take you some time to heal. You have a little bacta in your pack—you can use it now or you can save it for later, just in case something else happens to you. If you choose to save it for later, subtract 1 from your strength# for the rest of this adventure.

*NOTE: This counts as one of three Power uses you are allowed on this adventure.

To dodge the sparks (without using Power): Roll the 20-dice. Your roll# + your stealth# + your strength# is your adventure#.

If your adventure# is equal to or more than 14, add the difference + 15 to your AP total. You leap into the sand as quick as a rusty droid would leap into an oil bath. You may proceed.

If your adventure# is less than 14 but more than or equal to 9, subtract the difference from your AP total. The exploding sparks nearly ignite your head. Hopefully, the burnt-hair look will be in this year. The force of the blast knocks you into the sand. You may proceed.

If your adventure# is less than 9, subtract 30 from your AP total. Ouch! You're burnt pretty seriously. It's going to take you some time to heal. You have a little bacta in your pack—you can use it now or you can save it for later, just in case something else happens to you. If you choose to save it for later, subtract 1 from your strength# for the rest of this adventure.

After the droids short out, you push back to the surface of the sand, ears ringing. You try to imagine what it sounded like above-ground.

You listen for more sounds of pursuit from the capture droids. You hear none.

You move into the larger pipe. It is only a hand-span wider than the one you've just come through, but it feels much larger.

The current is surprisingly strong. Sand swirls all around you.

It pushes you along rapidly. You reach the pipe and see the Ghostling child in front of you trying frantically to scramble up it. But sand is rushing from the pipe, creating a strong current, and Ghostlings are so frail. The Ghostling can't make it up!

The child kicks and pushes furiously against the side of the pipes, but the current wins, pushing him off farther into the drainage system.

You reach the pipe and try to push yourself up. Sand roars all around you. It is a torrent. You need to follow the current and catch up with the Ghostling children.

The sand hurls you through the pipes, shoving and jostling you, a real flood.

You can't stop. You can't even slow down. You drop the tool bag with the ion blaster and the beamdrill. You can only slide along as best you can, clinging to your glow rod.

The other children all slip ahead faster than you do. You lose sight of them. You have no idea how fast you are going, or how far.

The raging drifts sweep you along for perhaps a thousand meters, past opening after opening, drainpipes that could lead anywhere.

Suddenly the pipe disappears, and the sand pushes you into a chasm. You go flying headlong into a deep dune.

To dive into the dune: Roll the 10-dice. Your roll# + your strength# + your skill# is your adventure#.

If your adventure# is equal to or more than 7, add the difference + 7 to your AP total. You slip into the sand gracefully. You may proceed.

If your adventure# is less than 7, subtract 15 from your AP total. You hit the sand hard and are temporarily stunned. Subtract 1 from your strength# for the next two confrontations. You may proceed.

You land in a mass of churning sand, and strike the stone bottom of the chamber. The blow forces the air from your lungs, and you accidentally knock off your sandmask.

You manage to cling onto your glow rod. In the depths below, you reach for your bag with the Jawa ion blaster and the other supplies in it. But your ribs are hurting badly.

You leave the bag behind and gasp for breathable air. Once there, you cough until your lungs clear. Choose to either find and retrieve your sandmask with or without using Power or retrieve the bag.

To find and retrieve your sandmask (using Power*): Choose your Find Power. You take a deep breath and plunge down to find your sandmask. Roll the 10-dice. Your roll# + your strength# + your Power# + your Power's mid-resist# is your adventure#. (Remember, if you are stunned, subtract 1 from your strength# for this encounter.)

If your adventure# is equal to or more than 8, add the difference + 12 to your AP total. The sandmask is yours again. You put it back on and proceed. If you haven't already retrieved your bag, you must proceed to do so now (below).

If your adventure# is less than 8, subtract the difference from your AP total. You run out of air before you can find the sandmask. To try again and take a deep breath, roll the 10-dice again. Your new roll# + your strength# + your Power# + your Power's mid-resist# + 1 is your new adventure#. (Remember, if you are stunned, subtract 1 from your strength# for this encounter.)

> *If your new adventure# is equal to or more than 8,* add the difference to your AP total. The sandmask is yours again. You put it back on and proceed. If you haven't already retrieved your bag, you must proceed to do so now (below).

> *If your new adventure# is less than 8,* subtract 20 from your AP total. The sandmask is gone. You will have to proceed without it. If you haven't already retrieved your bag, you must proceed to do so now (below).

*NOTE: This counts as one of three Power uses you are allowed on this adventure.

To find and retrieve your sandmask (without using Power): You take a deep breath and plunge down to find your sandmask. Roll the 10-dice. If tracking is one of your talents, your roll# + your strength# + your stealth# + 1 is your adventure#. If tracking is not one of your talents, your roll# + your strength# + your stealth# is your adventure#. (Remember, if you are stunned, subtract 1 from your strength# for this encounter.)

If your adventure# is equal to or more than 8, add the difference + 12 to your AP total. The sandmask is yours again. You put it back on and proceed. If you haven't already retrieved your bag, you must proceed to do so now (below).

If your adventure# is less than 8, subtract the difference from your AP total. You run out of air before you can find the sandmask. To try again and take a deep breath, roll the 10-dice again. If tracking is one of your talents, your new roll# + your strength# + your stealth# + 2 is your new adventure#. If tracking is not one of your talents, your new roll# + your strength# + your stealth# + 1 is your new adventure#. (Remember, if you are stunned, subtract 1 from your strength# for this encounter.)

If your new adventure# is equal to or more than 8, add the difference to your AP total. The sandmask is yours again. You put it back on and proceed. If you haven't already retrieved your bag, you must proceed to do so now (below).

If your new adventure# is less than 8, subtract 20 from your AP total. The sandmask is gone. You will have to proceed without it. If you haven't already retrieved your bag, you must proceed to do so now (below).

To retrieve the bag: Roll the 20-dice. If you have already recovered your sandmask, your roll# + your strength# + your skill# + 2 is your adventure#. If you have not recovered your sandmask, your roll# + your strength# + your skill# is your adventure#. (Remember, if you are stunned, subtract 1 from your strength# for this encounter.)

If your adventure# is equal to or more than 13, add the difference + 10 to your AP total. You wriggle through the sand and retrieve the bag. If you haven't already tried to find your sandmask, go back "To find and retrieve your sandmask (without using Power) (above). If you have your sandmask, you may proceed.

If your adventure# is less than 13, subtract the difference from your AP total. You push through the sand slowly. You're going to have to do better than that. Roll the 20-dice again. If you have already recovered your sandmask, your new roll# + your strength# + your skill# + 3 is your new adventure#. If you have not recovered your sandmask, your new roll# + your strength# + your skill# + 1 is your new adventure#. (Remember, if you are stunned, subtract 1 from your strength# for this encounter.)

If your new adventure# is equal to or more than 13, add the difference to your AP total. The bag is yours again. If you haven't already tried to find your sandmask, go back "To find and retrieve your sandmask (without using Power) (above). If you have your sandmask, you may proceed.

If your new adventure# is less than 13, subtract 7 from your AP total. Close…but not quite. Go back "To retrieve the bag," and repeat until you've retrieved the supplies.

In the shadows far from your glow rod, you see something: The claws of some monster that seems shy of the light.

It spurts forward.

An orange leg grasps your arm, and another twines around the glow rod.

A rock wart!

It is trying to pull the glow rod away.

To pull your glow rod from the rock wart: Roll the 20-dice. Your roll# + your strength# + your stealth# + 1 is your adventure#. (Remember, if you are stunned, subtract 1 from your strength# for this encounter.)

If your adventure# is equal to or more than 14, add the difference + 10 to your AP total. You rip the glow rod from its claw and may proceed.

If your adventure# is less than 14, subtract 10 from your AP total. The rock wart rips the glow rod from your hand. You need to get it back. Go back "To pull your glow rod from the rock wart," and repeat until you have it back.

The rock wart wraps its six legs around your neck.

You struggle with the monster, wishing that you had some kind of weapon. But all of your tools are in the bag, and you're not exactly in the position to search through it.

Choose to either evade the rock wart with or without using Power, or fight the rock wart.

To evade the rock wart (using Power)*: Choose your Confusion Power. Roll the 10-dice to escape the sandworm. Your roll# + your strength# + your Power# + your Power's mid-resist# is your adventure#. (Note: if you were stunned earlier, you no longer have to subtract 1 from your strength#. But if you were injured, you must still subtract 1, unless you healed yourself with bacta.)

If your adventure# is equal to or more than 7, add the difference + 15 to your AP total. You discover that you have a talent for escaping tight squeezes. You must have gotten it from learning how to squirm away from your aunt Urma when she tried to give you hugs. You may proceed.

If your adventure# is less than 7, subtract the difference from your AP total. The rock wart wraps two legs around your throat, and two around your stomach. With the very last of its legs, it begins tickling your armpits.

You've got to get out of here fast. Proceed to fight the rock wart (below).

*NOTE: This counts as one of three Power uses you are allowed on this adventure.

To evade the rock wart (without using Power): Roll the 20-dice to escape from its grasp. If defense is one of your talents, your roll# + your strength# + your stealth# + 1 is your adventure#. If defense is not one of your talents, your roll# + your strength# + your stealth# is your adventure#. (Note: If you were stunned earlier, you no longer have to subtract 1 from your strength#. But if you were injured, you must still subtract 1, unless you healed yourself with bacta.)

If your adventure# is equal to or more than 13, add the difference + 25 to your AP total. You artfully manage to slip away from its many legs. It whimpers and burrows away. You may proceed.

If your adventure# is less than 13, subtract the difference from your AP total. The rock wart chokes the stuffing out of you. Proceed to fight the rock wart (below).

To fight the rock wart: Roll the 20-dice. Since your hands are tied by tentacles, you're going to have to use your teeth. If you have a sandmask, it's only getting in your way. If you have a sandmask, your roll# + your strength# + your stealth# is your adventure#. If you didn't get your sandmask back, your roll# + your strength# + your stealth# + 2 is your adventure#.

If your adventure# is equal to or more than 13, add the difference + 11 to your AP total. You chomp into the rock wart's rubbery flesh. Hmmm...it tastes just like fish! You start to wonder if maybe you could sell some of this monster to one of the local restaurants. As if it can read your mind, the rock wart flees. You may proceed.

If your adventure# is less than 13, subtract the difference from your AP total. The good news is that there are still plenty of legs for you to bite. The bad news is that the rock wart is squeezing the stuffing out of you. After years of brushing your teeth, now is the time to put them to good use. To take another bite until this monster lets you go, roll the 20-dice again. Since your sandmask is now out of your way, your new roll# + your strength# + your stealth# + 2 is your new adventure#.

If your new adventure# is equal to or more than 12, add the difference to your AP total. The rock wart squirms away. You may proceed.

If your new adventure# is less than 12, subtract 30 from your AP total. The rock wart smothers you into brief unconsciousness. Then, happy with its work, it heads away. If you have not used it already, you have a little bacta in your pack—you can use it now or you can save it for later, just in case something else happens to you. If you have already used it, or if you choose to save it for later, subtract 1 from your strength# for the rest of this adventure.

The monster shrieks, making a strange sound in the pipes. Then it burrows away.

You grasp your tool bag, push back up to the surface, and raise your glow rod in order to get your bearings.

You and the other children have all emerged in a large chamber, perhaps eighty meters long and forty wide. The low ceiling is cut from stone.

Dozens of pipes open into the chamber. It seems to serve as some kind of catch basin where large objects can be cleared from the drainage.

In the dune around you, you see the Ghostling children. One child is coughing badly. It is the small boy that you have been following. The boy raises his head feebly, and begins to sink into the sand.

To rescue the Ghostling child: Roll the 10-dice. Your roll# + your strength# + your stealth# + 1 is your adventure#.

If your adventure# is equal to or more than 8, add the difference + 10 to your AP total. You grab the child from behind, wrap a hand over his shoulder and under his armpit, and begin to push to safety. Next time they have a life-saving class at the local Mos Espa desert, you'll be able to demonstrate how to do it properly. You may proceed.

If your adventure# is less than 8, subtract the difference from your AP total. The child fights from your grasp, trying to save himself, and struggles to climb atop you. However, you're smart enough to realize that you never let the kid you're trying to rescue climb on your shoulders. To take control of the child and try again, go back "To rescue the Ghostling child," and repeat until the boy is saved.

"Over here!" one of the Ghostling children shouts. In the corner of the dune is a landing of sorts, a solid spot where everyone can sit for a moment.

"Get out of the sand!" you warn. "There's something down here with us!"

You try to drag the little boy with you.

The children all struggle in terror, thrashing in the sand, until they reach the landing. They launch themselves onto it.

You get the child to safety.

"There's a monster in here?" one of your friends asks.

"Yeah," you say. "And it tastes awful."

"What do we do if it comes after us?" one of the Ghostling children asks. He can't hide the terror in his voice.

"I bit it pretty hard," you say. "That scared it away—at least for now. You can all take a bite if it comes back."

You wrestle the little boy onto the landing. The child can't stop coughing.

You realize he's hurt, and you don't know how to get out of here. You're in deep trouble!

You feel so tired, you can barely move.

"I'll find a way out of here," you offer at last. You can't let your friends down.

"Hurry," one of the Ghostlings begs. "We don't have much time. It won't take them long to follow us through this pipe."

You nod.

You look up at the array of pipes that empty into the chamber. There are dozens to choose from.

You pick one at random—a big one just overhead. The other children boost you up to it, and hand you the tool bag.

You take out the beamdrill. The power level on it is getting low, but you have a feeling that you'll need it. The beamdrill can cut through just about anything: rock, duracrete—even armor plate.

All you need to do is find a drainpipe that leads up into an empty room, and then cut your way out.

You inch through the pipe. There isn't much sand here. Wherever this pipe leads, it hasn't been used in a long time.

Perfect, you think. You imagine a safe, abandoned warehouse.

You continue crawling along, clunking with your shoes and bag of tools. The pipe takes you uphill to a Y-shaped intersection. You look up the left end, and then the right.

You don't know which way to go. You turn off your glow rod for a second to see if you can spot light in either direction. If you could see a light, then it would mean that the tunnel is coming to an end.

No sooner have you powered down the glow rod than you hear a growling from the pipe on your right. You've heard that sound before: womp rats!

The dirty rodents live all over Tatooine. A full-grown womp rat can be as long as a man. They are big enough to carry off children and even full-grown Jawas.

Desperately, you try to think what to do. You don't have a blaster, and you doubt that a womp rat would be scared of your teeth.

All you have is your beamdrill.

You fumble with its controls in the dark. You want to set the plasma beam for a long, narrow ray.

To adjust the settings on the beamdrill:
Roll the 10-dice. Your roll# + your skill# is your adventure#.

If your adventure# is equal to or more than 6, add the difference + 4 to your AP total. You expertly adjust the settings. You may proceed.

If your adventure# is less than 6, subtract the difference from your AP total. You fool around for a moment. The giant rodents are traveling closer. Go back "To adjust the settings on the beamdrill," and repeat until you have the right setting.

The womp rats race closer. You can hear their feet pounding the metal pipe. You scream, hoping they will slow down or back off.

For a fraction of a second, it works.

You swing the nozzle of the beamdrill up. You pull the trigger on the beam actuator. A searing white stream of superheated gas sprays from the beamdrill. It acts like a flame-thrower. You must try to fry a womp rat.

To fry a womp rat: Choose your beamdrill. Roll the 10-dice. Your roll# + your weaponry# + the beamdrill's mid-range# is your adventure#.

If your adventure# is equal to or more than 8, add the difference + 15 to your AP total. That womp rat is toast! You may proceed.

If your adventure# is less than 8, subtract the difference from your AP total. You miss the womp rat and only manage to warm the pipe. The womp rat tiptoes toward you over the sizzling pipe. Roll the 10-dice again. Your new roll# + your weaponry# + the beamdrill's close-range# is your new adventure#.

If your new adventure# is equal to or more than 8, add the difference + 15 to your AP total. That womp rat is toast! You may proceed.

If your new adventure# is less than 8, subtract the difference from your AP total. Very bad news. The womp rat got you. Your adventure is over. You must go back to the beginning of this adventure and begin as a new character.

Up the tunnel, you see the womp rat's fierce red eyes reflected in the beam's light. It growls and bares its enormous incisors, just as the beamdrill slices through it!

The other womp rats in the pack snarl and back away. You wriggle into the left fork of the tunnel, eager to escape.

You follow the pipe. A dozen times it twists and meets with other pipes.

Each time it does, you are careful to take the handle of your glow rod and scratch an X into the rust overhead, so that you'll know how to get back.

Finally, you reach a juncture and see a drainpipe straight overhead.

You turn off your glow rod as you draw near, then sit beneath the pipe for a second, listening. The room overhead seems quiet. You squeeze yourself into the pipe, climb up until you near the drain. The drain cover overhead is secured with rusted bolts. If you hit them, they might snap.

You must knock the drain cover open either with or without using your beamdrill.

To knock the drain cover open (using your beamdrill): Roll the 20-dice. Your roll# + your weaponry# + your beamdrill's close-range# is your adventure#.

If your adventure# is equal to or more than 12, add the difference + 5 to your AP total. You easily punch the drain cover open. You may proceed.

If your adventure# is less than 12, subtract the difference from your AP total. It's going to take some more power. Go back "To knock the drain cover open (using your beamdrill)," and repeat until you've opened the cover.

To knock the drain cover open (without using your beamdrill): Roll the 20-dice. Your roll# + your strength# + 2 is your adventure#.

If your adventure# is equal to or more than 13, add the difference + 10 to your AP total. You easily punch the drain cover open. You may proceed.

If your adventure# is less than 13, subtract the difference from your AP total. Oof! You guess the bolts aren't as weak as they seem. Proceed to use your beamdrill (above).

A bolt breaks with a clank. You giggle and think to yourself: *They haven't made a drainage system yet that I can't break out of!*

Suddenly, in the room above, you hear a door *whoosh* open.

Someone whispers in Huttese, "Did you hear that?" The voice sounds mechanical, almost like a droid's vocoder.

"What?" a similar voice asks.

"There's someone in here!"

You hold still, not daring to move.

A light snaps on. Two figures creep into the room overhead. You can see them through the grate. They are Morseerians—creatures with green skin, long lumpy heads, and four arms. Since Morseerians are methane breathers, they both wear goggles and breathers. The speakers on the breathers make their voices sound mechanical.

You recognize the two immediately. You've seen them around Mos Espa. They are space pirates. The room overhead is a large storage room that once housed heavy cleaning equipment.

The pirates begin to search the room, shining strong beam lights into the corners. You quietly slide down farther into the pipe.

"Hey," one of the pirates says. "Look at that drain cover. Someone's been working at it."

Desperately, you drop down the pipe as quietly as possible. Overhead, the light flashes about as the pirates near.

Choose to either avoid detection with or without using Power.

To avoid detection (using Power)*: Choose your Infiltration Power or your Hide Power. Roll the 20-dice. Your roll# + your Power# + your Power's high-resist# + your stealth# is your adventure#.

If your adventure# is equal to or more than 12, add the difference + 13 to your AP total. You've seen rocks that make more noise than you do. You may proceed.

If your adventure# is less than 12, subtract the difference from your AP total. You're sneaking along quite nicely, when you suddenly your stomach grumbles. Let's just hope that the Morseerians mistake it for the sound of a distant explosion. You may proceed.

*NOTE: This counts as one of three Power uses you are allowed on this adventure.

To avoid detection (without using Power): Roll the 20-dice. If hiding is one of your talents, your roll# + your stealth# + 4 is your adventure#. If hiding is not one of your talents, your roll# + your stealth# + 2 is your adventure#.

If your adventure# is equal to or more than 12, add the difference + 11 to your AP total. You move as quietly as a space slug hiding in its burrow. You may proceed.

If your adventure# is less than 12, subtract 10 from you AP total. Your knees bang against the pipe like drumsticks against a drum. Luckily, the pirates don't hear you. Go back "To avoid detection (without using Power)," and try again.

Your feet touch ground, and you slither to safety just as a wrenching noise comes from above. Rust and dirt drift down through a strong beam of light.

You hide in the dark. You hardly dare to breathe. The Morseerians are as big as humans, but with larger heads and shoulders. They won't be able to crawl down the pipe.

"Think someone has been trying to break in here?" one of the Morseerians asks.

The pirates seem mighty suspicious. You are afraid. Suddenly, you have a brilliant idea!

You try to remember exactly how the womp rat had growled. You feel back low in your throat. You must make a noise like a womp rat.

To make a noise like a womp rat: Roll the 10-dice. If communication is one of your talents, your roll# + your skill# + your charm# + 2 is your adventure#. If communication is not one of your talents, your roll# + your skill# + your charm# is your adventure#.

If your adventure# is equal to or more than 8, add the difference + 6 to your AP total. You make a convincing noise like a womp rat, hungry for blood! You may proceed.

If your adventure# is less than 8, subtract 5 from you AP total. You really sound more like a worrt with indigestion than a womp rat. Try again, and this time put your spleen into it! Go back "To make a noise like a womp rat," and repeat.

For heart-pounding seconds, you wait for the pirate's reactions.

"What's that?" one of the pirates asks. "A sick worrt?"

"Nah, dirty womp rat vermin, I think," the other pirate grumbles.

"Whatever it is," the other pirate says, "I'm going to shoot it!"

Suddenly a blinding blue light erupts in front of your eyes. A sizzling blaster bolt slams into the pipe. Shards of hot metal and bits of rust fly up.

Choose to either avoid getting blinded by the blaster bolt with or without using Power.

To evade the attack (using Power)*: Choose your Reflex Power. Roll the 20-dice to protect your eyes. Your roll# + your stealth# +

your Power# + your Power's low-resist# is your adventure#.

If your adventure# is equal to or more than 13, add the difference + 8 to your AP total. Who needs a blast helmet with eyes like yours? You're safe, and may proceed.

If your adventure# is less than 13, subtract the difference from your AP total. The flash of light burns your eyes. You are going to have trouble seeing now. Subtract 1 from your skill# for the rest of this adventure. You may proceed.

*NOTE: This counts as one of three Power uses you are allowed on this adventure.

To avoid getting blinded (without using Power): Roll the 20-dice to dodge the attack. Your roll# + your strength# + your stealth# is your adventure#.

If your adventure# is equal to or more than 13, add the difference + 8 to your AP total. You turn away from the blinding blaster bolt just in time. You may proceed.

If your adventure# is less than 13, subtract the difference from your AP total. The flash of light burns your eyes. You are going to have trouble seeing now. Subtract 1 from your skill# for the rest of this adventure. You may proceed.

"Think you got him?" a pirate asks.

"Doubt it," a Morseerian says. "But I'll bet he doesn't come around here again. Better check the money, just to make sure."

You sit blinking dirt from your eyes, hardly daring to breathe. Overhead you hear a clanking noise, the squeaking of hinges, and the sudden rattle as someone picks up a handful of coins.

"Looks good to me," one of the pirates says.

You hear a noise overhead as the pirates put the grate back on. They use their boots to stomp it snugly into place.

Your heart races. Your breathing comes shallow. That blaster bolt almost hit you!

You rub at your eyes. They're full of grit. You want to get out of here fast. But something holds you back: pirate treasure!

You've stumbled onto the Morseerians' treasure room.

You're an honest kid. But you need money desperately. Jira has already contacted the smugglers, and they'll be here within the hour to take the Ghostling children home. But first they will want money!

Now you've stumbled upon some.

You can't leave without it.

You wait several moments for the pirates to leave. As stealthily as you can, you wriggle back up the pipe until you reach the drain cover.

Choose to either sneak up the pipe with or without using Power.

To sneak up the pipe (using Power)*:
Choose your Movement Power. Roll the 20-dice. Your roll# + your strength# + your Power# + your Power's low-resist# is your adventure#.

If your adventure# is equal to or more than 16, add the difference + 10 to your AP total. Oh, you're a sneaky one! You may proceed.

If your adventure# is less than 16, subtract the difference from your AP total. You lose your footing and slip down the pipe. To climb back up the pipe, roll the 20-dice again. Your new roll# + your Power# + your Power's low-resist# + your stealth# + your strength# is your new adventure#.

If your new adventure# is equal to or more than 15, add the difference to your AP total. You're back where you started. Go back "To sneak up the pipe (using Power)," and repeat until you make it up.

If your new adventure# is less than 15, subtract 10 from you AP total. You need to try harder. Go back "To climb back up the pipe," and repeat until you're back where you started, then climb up again.

*NOTE: This counts as one of three Power uses you are allowed on this adventure.

To sneak up the pipe (without using Power): Roll the 20-dice to sneak up the pipe. If climbing is one of your talents, your roll# + your stealth# + your strength# + 2 is your adventure#. If climbing is not one of your talents, your roll# + your stealth# + your strength# is your adventure#.

If your adventure# is equal to or more than 13, add the difference + 10 to your AP total. You're as quiet as a dead Hutt. You may proceed.

If your adventure# is less than 13, subtract 10 from you AP total. You lose your footing and slip down the pipe. To climb back up the pipe, roll the 20-dice again. If climbing is one of your talents, your new roll# + your stealth# + your strength# + 3 is your new adventure#. If climbing is not one of your talents, your new roll# + your stealth# + your strength# + 1 is your new adventure#.

If your new adventure# is equal to or more than 13, add the difference to your AP total. You're back where you started. Go back "To sneak up the pipe (without using Power)," and repeat until you make it up.

If your new adventure# is less than 13, subtract 10 from you AP total. You need to try harder. Go back "To climb back up the pipe," and repeat until you're back where you started, then climb up again.

Sweat pours off of you. Climbing up the pipe quietly is hard work.

You push the cover gently and it comes off. The Morseerian pirates have actually broken the bolts for you! You feel tempted to thank them.

You carefully lift the heavy iron cover, then slide it across the floor. In seconds, you enter the storage room.

There is no light. You flip on your glow rod and look around. Old crates, most of them covered in dust, fill the room.

An old air cooler is built into a niche over the door, but it doesn't work. The room feels stiflingly hot.

You wonder where the treasure is. You look on the floor. No one has cleaned it for decades. It, too, is covered with dust. It isn't hard to figure out where the pirates have hidden the treasure box. You try to follow their footprints in the dust.

To find the treasure: Roll the 10-dice. If tracking is one of your talents, your roll# + your skill# + 3 is your adventure#. If tracking is not one of your talents, your roll# + your skill# + 1 is your adventure#.

If your adventure# is equal to or more than 6, add the difference + 5 to your AP total. Tracking the pirates across this dusty floor is as easy as tracking a bantha across mud flats.

If your adventure# is less than 6, subtract the difference from your AP total. You can't find it. Go back "To find the treasure," and repeat to keep searching for the treasure.

You reach some boxes covered by a tarp. You gently lift the cover. Beneath the tarp is a locked freight box. The treasure!

Your heart pounds in terror. You grip your beamdrill as if it were a blaster, afraid that the pirates will come back at any moment. You try not to imagine what they'll do if they catch you.

You try to lift the box, but it's so heavy that you doubt that even a hulking Whiphid could budge it.

You don't have a key for the lock.

But you do have a beamdrill.

You adjust the settings on the drill so that it will emit a small, narrow beam of plasma. You flip on the power. The drill hisses like a snake, and emits a steady blue tongue of flame.

You aim the beam into the lock, begin to cut through it. The metal turns red and molten, drips into a puddle on the floor. You've used a beamdrill before, but this is the first time you've ever cut into a freight box. Proceed to open the lock.

To open the lock: Roll the 10-dice. If lock bypass is one of your talents, your roll# + your skill# + your beamdrill's close-range# + 2 is your adventure#. If lock bypass is not one of your talents, your roll# + your skill# + your beamdrill's close-range# is your adventure#.

If your adventure# is equal to or more than 7, add the difference + 10 to your AP total. You cut through the lock so easily that a suspicious person might think you did this kind of thing all the time. You may proceed.

If your adventure# is less than 7, subtract the difference from your AP total. The lock is boobytrapped! A tiny security droid pops out from behind the box and attacks you with a blaster beam. You must turn the beamdrill up and destroy the droid before it can alert the pirates. Roll the 20-dice. Your new roll# + your weaponry# + your beamdrill's close-range# is your new adventure#.

If your new adventure# is equal to or more than 12, add the difference to your AP total. You've defeated the security droid. To concentrate on opening the box, roll the 10-dice for your newest roll#. Your new roll# + your skill# + your beamdrill's close-range# is your new adventure#.

If your new adventure# is equal to or more than 7, add the difference to your AP total. You cut through the lock so easily that a suspicious person might think you did this kind of thing all the time. You may proceed.

If your new adventure# is less than 7, subtract the difference from your AP total. Go back "To concentrate on opening the box," and repeat until you have opened the lock.

If your new adventure# is less than 12, subtract 30 from your AP total. The security droid blasts you! Pushing though the pain, you aim your beamdrill again, and blast the droid back. He's defeated. Go back "To open the lock," and repeat until the lock opens.

In seconds, you flip open the lid.

Inside the box is a fortune in coins from a hundred worlds!

Here on Tatooine, people use hard currency all the time. You know the worth of many of the pieces. You start grabbing the most valuable coins and shoving them into the deep pockets of your Jawa robe. They *clink* softly, making music to your ears.

You have come across quite a treasure. Reward yourself by adding 100 to your AP total.

You quickly count out a good three thousand wupiupi worth of coins.

But you haven't counted on how keen the ears of the Morseerian pirates might be!

You hear a scuffling noise at the door.

Choose to evade the pirates with or without using Power.

To evade the pirates (using Power)*: Choose your Hide Power. Roll the 20-dice to leap for cover. Your roll# + your stealth# + your Power# + your Power's mid-resist# is your adventure#.

If your adventure# is equal to or more than 12, add the difference + 7 to your AP total. You slip into the dark as quietly as a shadow. The pirates cannot see you. You may proceed.

If your adventure# is less than 12, subtract the difference from your AP total. You stumble and trip as you dive for cover. In moments, the pirates will have you cornered. Proceed quickly.

*NOTE: This counts as one of three Power uses you are allowed on this adventure.

To evade the pirates (without using Power): Roll the 20-dice to hide quickly. If hiding is one of your talents, your roll# + your stealth# + 2 is your adventure#. If hiding is not one of your talents, your roll# + your stealth# is your adventure#.

If your adventure# is equal to or more than 13, add the difference + 10 to your AP total. You leap for cover as quietly as a shadow. You may proceed.

If your adventure# is less than 13, subtract the difference from your AP total. The keen-eared pirates know you're here, and it's just a matter of time until they hunt you down. Proceed quickly.

The Morseerians flash their light beam over the room.

"Look," a pirate says. "The grate's off the floor. I told you someone is in here!"

You stifle the urge to scream. These pirates have blasters. They won't hesitate to shoot!

The pirates stand in the doorway. You hide behind the crates and fumble once again with the settings on the beamdrill.

You set it to maximum length, wide beam. At these settings, the drill will act like a flame-thrower, shooting a wide beam of fire across the room. But you can tell by the weight of the drill that the fuel tank is almost empty. At these settings, the fuel will pour out quickly.

You wait until the light beams are trained on the far side of the room, then rise up in the darkness.

You don't want to shoot the pirates, because you know that if you do, the methane tanks on their breathers will blow up! You only want to scare them. You leap from cover, shout, aim the beamdrill over the heads of the pirates, and pull the trigger.

To frighten the pirates: Roll the 20-dice. If your hair got burned earlier, you look extra scary right now, and your roll# + your weaponry# + your beamdrill's far-range# + 2 is your adventure#. If your hair is fine, your roll# + your weaponry# + your beamdrill's far-range# is your adventure#.

If your adventure# is equal to or more than 14, add the difference + 20 to your AP total. You leap out from behind the chests, screaming like someone in Gardulla the Hutt's torture chamber. You are covered in sand, and fire fills the room. The Morseerians shout, "Augh, sand warts!" and retreat. You may proceed.

If your adventure# is less than 14, subtract the difference from your AP total. You need to get closer—but not too close. Roll the 20-dice again. If your hair got burned earlier, you look extra scary right now, and your new roll# + your weaponry# + your beamdrill's mid-range# + 2 is your new adventure#. If your hair is fine, your new roll# + your weaponry# + your beamdrill's mid-range# is your new adventure#.

If your new adventure# is equal to or more than 15, add the difference to your AP total. You leap out from behind the chests, screaming like someone in Gardulla the Hutt's torture chamber. You are covered in sand, and fire fills the room. The Morseerians shout, "Augh, sand warts!" and retreat. You may proceed.

If your new adventure# is less than 15, subtract 10 from you AP total. The pirates are digging in. You are going to have to escape even though they haven't retreated. Keep this in mind for the next confrontation. You may proceed.

The rays arc out of your beamdrill, flooding the room with light. The Morseerians scream.

You haven't counted on the fact that the pirates have four arms. Each pirate has a beam light, but each also holds two blasters.

Both pirates open fire as they head to the door. Green blaster bolts sizzle through the air, blowing crates into pieces of flying debris, tearing through the walls, burning past your feet.

You scream and rush at the pirates, even as they back out the door, fleeing in terror.

You keep the flame shooting at the door as you race for the drain. The beamdrill suddenly sputters empty. You hurl the drill through the doorway and must dive headfirst down into the drain.

To dive down the drain: Roll the 10-dice. If you made the pirates retreat earlier, your roll# + your stealth# + 2 is your adventure#. If the pirates did not retreat, and instead were digging in, your roll# + your stealth# is your adventure#.

If your adventure# is equal to or more than 9, add the difference + 10 to your AP total. If you get out of this, you should join a diving team. You may proceed.

If your adventure# is less than 9, subtract the difference from your AP total. You wriggle and squirm, trying to get down the pipe. Maybe you shouldn't have filled your pockets with all of those coins. The pirates are gaining on you. Roll the 10-dice again. If you made the pirates retreat earlier, your new roll# + your stealth# + 2 is your new adventure#. If the pirates did not retreat, and instead were digging in, your new roll# + your stealth# is your new adventure#.

If your new adventure# is equal to or more than 8, add the difference + 10 to your AP total. You dive to safety, and may proceed.

If your new adventure# is less than 8, subtract 30 from your AP total. The pirates have caught you. Proceed to persuade them to let you go with or without using Power (below).

To persuade the pirates to let you go (using Power)*: Choose your Persuasion Power or your Confusion Power. You tell the pirates you are just an exterminator, sent to clear the area of womp rats. Roll the 20-dice. Your roll# + your charm# + your Power# + your Power's mid-resist# is your adventure#.

If your adventure# is equal to or more than 7, add the difference to your AP total. When the pirates go to check the box to see if anyone has tampered with it, you duck into the pipe. You may proceed.

If your adventure# is less than 7, subtract the difference from your AP total. The pirates don't believe you. You're caught—and trapped. The pirates lock you in a box and leave the room to check if there's a reward on your head. To break out of the chest and escape, roll the 20-dice again. Your new roll# + your strength# + your skill# is your new adventure#.

If your new adventure# is equal to or more than 13, add the difference to your AP total. You break out of the box and dive to safety. You may proceed.

If your new adventure# is less than 13 but equal to or more than 10, add the difference to your AP total. The lock is beginning to budge. Go back "To break out of the chest and escape," and try again.

If your new adventure# is less than 10, subtract 50 from your AP total. There's no escape. The pirates have got you and they're not going to let you go. Your adventure is over. Go back to the beginning and start over as a new character.

*NOTE: This counts as one of three Power uses you are allowed on this adventure.

To persuade the pirates to let you go (without using Power): You tell the pirates you are just an exterminator, sent to clear the area of womp rats. Roll the 10-dice. If charm is one of your talents, your roll# + your charm# + 2 is your adventure#. If charm is not one of your talents, your roll# + your charm# is your adventure#.

If your adventure# is equal to or more than 7, add the difference to your AP total. When the pirates go to check the box to see if anyone has tampered with it, you duck into the pipe. You may proceed.

If your adventure# is less than 7, subtract the difference from your AP total. The pirates don't believe you. You're caught—and trapped. The pirates lock you in a box and leave the room to check if there's a reward on your head. To break out of the box and escape, roll the 20-dice. Your new roll# + your strength# + your skill# is your new adventure#.

If your new adventure# is equal to or more than 12, add the difference to your AP total. You break out of the box and dive to safety. You may proceed.

If your new adventure# is less than 12, subtract 50 from your AP total. There's no escape. The pirates have got you and they're not going to let you go. Your adventure is over. Go back to the beginning and start over as a new character.

You barely avoid crushing your head as you dive down the pipe. You reach the bottom, and slide back down along the pipe you'd come through.

You scramble through the pipe as fast as you can. You don't know how soon the slave masters will come searching for you and your friends.

You only know that you have to find a way out of the drain system.

You reach a juncture, turn again, and find an old pipe. You climb upward and reach the drain cover. The pipe opens into a warehouse, where food crates are stacked all around. Lights are on.

You can only be in one place: the storage room for the Mos Espa Galactic Food Emporium—just down the street from Watto's junkyard!

You climb up to the drain cover, and push. Its bolts look old and rusted, but you can't get the leverage you need.

You try banging the bolts with the handle of your glow rod, hoping that it won't break before the bolts do.

A voice overhead demands, "What are you doing?"

You look up to see a huge man peering through the grate.

"Drain inspector," you say, coming up with the first lie that springs to your lips. "Could you give me a hand with this?"

The big man stares down at you, unbelieving. "Escaped slave is more like it," he says. "I should call security." He glances toward a nearby door.

You can't see the man well through the drain screen. He is just a rough outline. But slowly you began to pick out details of his clothes. The man wears a simple tunic made of cheap fabric, as dull as the sands of Tatooine. There is a familiar look to his face. He is weathered, beaten down by life. You have seen that look a thousand times on the faces of other slaves.

You must attempt to talk him into helping you either with or without using Power.

To talk the slave into helping you (using Power): Choose your Persuasion Power. Roll the 20-dice to convince him to help. Your roll# + your charm# + your Power# + your Power's mid-resist# is your adventure#.

If your adventure# is equal to or more than 13, add the difference + 15 to your AP total. The slave is reduced to tears as he listens to your plea for help. You may proceed.

If your adventure# is less than 13, subtract the difference from your AP total. The slave needs more convincing. You offer him some coins from your pocket. Go back "To talk the slave into helping you (using Power)," and try again, this time adding 1 more to your adventure#.

*NOTE: This counts as one of three Power uses you are allowed on this adventure.

To talk the slave into helping you (without using Power): Roll the 20-dice to convince the slave to help you. If charm is one of your talents, your roll# + your charm# + 3 is your adventure#. If charm is not one of your talents, your roll# + your charm# + 1 is your adventure#.

If your adventure# is equal to or more than 13, add the difference + 15 to your AP total. The slave takes pity on you, the most pitiful-looking of slaves. You may proceed.

If your adventure# is less than 13, subtract the difference from your AP total. The slave needs more convincing. You must wheedle, whine, and beg some more. Go back "To talk the slave into helping you (without using Power)," and repeat until the slave is willing to help.

"Please," you beg. "Help us!"

The fellow looks nervously at the door again.

"Go away," the slave begs. "I have a family to protect."

"First pull off the grate from the drain," you say.

"You'll get us all killed," the man objects.

"Pull off the grate and walk away. Don't come back for awhile," you suggest. "No one will ever know."

The fellow looks around nervously. Sweat breaks out on his brow.

"Please," you say. "They're just children I'm trying to save. All of them are kids."

The man reaches down and yanks the drain cover. There is the sound of twisting metal as it breaks from the floor. Only then do you realize how big the slave up there is. He is a strong man, with massive arms made hard by long hours of lifting and stacking crates. You could never have removed the drain cover without his help.

"You've got twenty minutes," the slave says. He walks out of the storage room and turns off the lights.

You scramble through the pipes as fast as you can, racing back to your friends.

As you do, you pass pipe after pipe. You stop briefly at each intersection to look for your marks. Choose to track the path either with or without using Power.

To track the path (using Power)*: Choose your Compass Power or Find Power. Roll the 20-dice. Your roll# + your navigation# + your Power# + your Power's low-resist# is your adventure#.

If your adventure# is equal to or more than 12, add the difference + 5 to your AP total. It's easy to find your glowing trail. You may proceed.

If your adventure# is less than 12, subtract the difference from your AP total. You momentarily get lost and have to search for the route. Go back "To track the path (using Power)," and repeat until you've found it.

*NOTE: This counts as one of three Power uses you are allowed on this adventure.

To track the path (without using Power): Roll the 10-dice. If tracking is one of your talents, your roll# + your skill# + 3 is your adventure#. If tracking is not one of your talents, your roll# + your skill# is your adventure#.

If your adventure# is equal to or more than 7, add the difference + 5 to your AP total. It's easy to find your glowing trail. You may proceed.

If your adventure# is less than 7, subtract the difference from your AP total. You momentarily get lost and have to search for the route. Go back "To track the path (without using Power)," and repeat until you've found it.

You reach the children and quickly lead them back up to the market—with only a minute or two left. Once everyone is out of the drainage system, you sneak out the back door of the warehouse.

You've been in the pipes for a long time. Night has begun to fall on Tatooine. The shadows are deep and thick.

The Ghostling children and your friends all hide behind the store.

You get Watto's landspeeder. (Luckily, he's away on business.) You bring it back, and the children all rush out of the shadows and hop in. You cover them with a dirty tarp.

Just then, you hear voices. At the back of the store, a door bursts open. Two attackers rush out with blaster rifles. Rodian slave hunters!

Choose to either deceive the slave hunters with or without using Power, evade the slave hunters with or without using Power, or hit the slave hunters with you vehicle.

To deceive the slave hunters (using Power): Choose your Persuasion Power or Confusion Power. Roll the 20-dice. Your roll# + your charm# + your Power# + your Power's mid-resist# is your adventure#.

If your adventure# is equal to or more than 13, add the difference + 12 to your AP total. You shout in Jawan, "Quick, they're in the drain pipes!" The Rodians don't understand a word of Jawan, but they understand your gestures, and bound off into the streets. You may proceed.

If your adventure# is less than 13, subtract the difference from your AP total. The hunters shout, "Stick up your hands, and we might not shoot!" You're not going to take that risk. Choose to either evade the slave hunters without using Power (below) or hit them with your vehicle (below).

*NOTE: This counts as one of three Power uses you are allowed on this adventure.

To deceive the slave hunters (without using Power): Roll the 20-dice. If charm is one of your talents, your roll# + your charm# + 2 is your adventure#. If charm is not one of your talents, your roll# + your charm# is your adventure#.

If your adventure# is equal to or more than 13, add the difference + 10 to your AP total. The slave hunters burst through the door. Since you are still wearing your Jawa robe, you shout, "Utini!" and point down the alley. The slave hunters bound away. You may proceed.

If your adventure# is less than 13, subtract the difference from your AP total. The slave hunters aren't complete idiots. They pull up their blasters and start blasting at you.

Choose to either evade them without using Power (below) or hit them with your vehicle (below).

To evade the slave hunters (using Power)*: Choose your Reflex Power or Defense Power. Roll the 20-dice to veer from the path of the gunfire and take off in the landspeeder. Your roll# + your navigation# + your vehicle's speed# + your Power# + your Power's low-resist# is your adventure#.

If your adventure# is equal to or more than 16, add the difference + 15 to your AP total. You scream past the Rodians so fast that you break the sound barrier. The sonic boom leaves them deaf for the next hour. You may proceed.

If your adventure# is less than 16, subtract 20 from your AP total. The hunters blow a hole in your landspeeder. You can go back "To evade the slave hunters (using Power)," to try to escape again, or try to hit the slave hunters with your vehicle (below).

*NOTE: This counts as one of three Power uses you are allowed on this adventure.

To evade the slave hunters (without using Power): You jump into the landspeeder. Roll the 20-dice to drive away from the pirates. If navigation is one of your talents, your roll# + your navigation# + your vehicle's speed# + 2 is your adventure#. If navigation is not one of your talents, your roll# + your navigation# + your vehicle's speed# is your adventure#.

If your adventure# is equal to or more than 13, add the difference + 12 to your AP total. You blow past the Rodians so fast, they're bowled over by the tailwind. You may proceed.

If your adventure# is less than 13, subtract 15 from your AP total. The hunters take a shot at you and blow a hole in your landspeeder. You can go back "To evade the slave hunters (without using Power)," to try to escape again, or you may try to hit the slave hunters with your vehicle (below).

To hit the slave hunters with your vehicle: Roll the 20-dice. If navigation is one of your talents, your roll# + your navigation# + your landspeeder's stealth# + 2 is your adventure#. If navigation is not one of your talents, your roll# + your navigation# + your landspeeder's stealth# is your adventure#.

If your adventure# is equal to or more than 14, add the difference + 12 to your AP total. You go screaming up to the store's loading dock in your landspeeder and knock the Rodians right off their feet. You may proceed.

If your adventure# is less than 14, subtract the difference from your AP total. You go screaming up the loading dock, but miss the hunters completely. They are still firing. To dodge their blasts and escape, roll the 20-dice again. If navigation is one of your talents, your new roll# + your navigation# + your landspeeder's stealth# + your landspeeder's speed# + 1 is your new adventure#. If navigation is not one of your talents, your new roll# + your navigation# + your landspeeder's stealth# + your landspeeder's speed# is your new adventure#.

If your new adventure# is equal to or more than 14, add the difference + 12 to your AP total. You escape the slave hunters and can bring your friends to safety. You may proceed.

If your adventure# is less than 14, subtract the difference from your AP total. Go back "To hit the slave hunters with your vehicle," and repeat until you're free.

Soon you leave Mos Espa far behind and drive out to Bantha Rock, where you meet the smugglers. It's time to get your friends and the Ghostling children off this planet!

Congratulations! You have helped the Ghostling children escape from the clutches of Gardulla the Hutt. Add 300 to your AP total.

To read the end of this adventure, please turn to page 94 of your Star Wars Adventures novel, *Trouble on Tatooine*.